Playing by the Rules

RULES FOR
LITTLE MC

• Be nice
the animals.

• Always be good.

Written by Jack Gabolinscy

Illustrated by Matthew Wilson

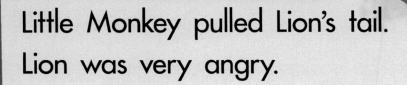

Little Monkey pulled Lion's tail.
Lion was very angry.

"Don't pull my tail!" he roared.

Little Monkey laughed,
but Mum was sad.

"Be a good monkey," she said.
"Follow the rules."

Little Monkey poked a beehive.
He made the bees very angry.

"Buzz! Buzz! Buzz!
Don't poke us!" they growled.

Little Monkey was happy,
but Mum was sad.

"Be a good monkey," she said.
"Follow the rules."

4

Little Monkey put banana peels
on the path.
Hippo slipped and fell
on her nose.
She was very angry.

"Don't drop peels!" she growled.

Little Monkey laughed,
but Mum was mad.

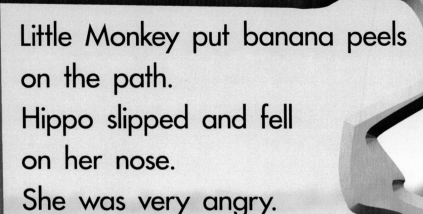

"Be a good monkey
and follow the rules," growled Mum.

But Little Monkey didn't want
to be good.
He didn't want to follow the rules.
He only wanted to play.
He was having a good time.

Little Monkey climbed up
Giraffe's neck and sat
on his head.
Giraffe was angry.

"Get down, now!" he growled.

Mum was angry, too.

"Be a good little monkey," she said.

Little Monkey tied Snake in a knot.

"Hiss! Hiss!
Let go! Let go!" Snake hissed.

Snake was mad.
Mum was sad.

"Won't you be a good little monkey?"
she asked.

RULES FOR GOOD
LITTLE MONKEYS
• Be nice to
   the animals.
• Always be good.

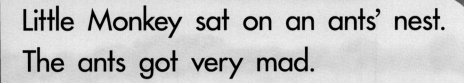

Little Monkey sat on an ants' nest.
The ants got very mad.

"Don't sit on our nest!"
they growled.

Bite! Bite! Bite!
They bit him on the toes.

"Help! Help! Help!"
cried Little Monkey.

Little Monkey was sad,
but Mum was happy.

"See what happens when you
break the rules?" she said.
"Will you be a good
little monkey now?"